NANCY DREW GRAPHIC NOVELS AVAILABLE FROM PAPERCUTZ

#1 "The Demon of River Heights"

#2 "Writ In Stone"

#3 "The Haunted Dollhouse"

#4 "The Girl Who Wasn't There"

#5 "The Fake Heir"

#6 "Mr. Cheeters Is Missing"

#7 "The Charmed Bracelet"

#8 "Global Warning"

#9 "Ghost In The Machinery"

#10 "The Disoriented Express"

#11 "Monkey Wrench Blues"

#12 "Dress Reversal"

#13 "Doggone Town"

#14 "Sleight of Dan"

Coming November '08 #15 "Tiger Counter"

$7.95 each in paperback, $12.95 each in hardcover.

Please add $4.00 for postage and handling for the first book, add $1.00 for each additional book.

Please make check payable to NBM Publishing. Send to:
Papercutz, 40 Exchange Place, Suite 1308 New York, NY 10005, 1-800-886-1223
www.papercutz.com

NANCY DREW

#14 DREW girl detective ®

Sleight of Dan

STEFAN PETRUCHA & SARAH KINNEY • Writers
SHO MURASE • Artist
with 3D CG elements and color by CARLOS JOSE GUZM
Based on the series by
CAROLYN KEENE

PAPERCUTZ
New York

Sleight of Dan
STEFAN PETRUCHA & SARAH KINNEY – Writers
SHO MURASE – Artist
with 3D CG elements and color by CARLOS JOSE GUZMAN
BRYAN SENKA – Letterer
MIKHAELA REID and MASHEKA WOOD – Production
JIM SALICRUP
Editor-in-Chief

ISBN 10: 1-59707-141-2 hardcover edition
ISBN 13: 978-1-59707-141-3 hardcover edition

Printed in China.

10   9   8   7   6   5   4   3   2   1

MOST FOLKS BELIEVE IN *SOME* KIND OF MAGIC. IT'S FUN TO BE MYSTIFIED BY STUFF THAT SEEMS IMPOSSIBLE.

BUT, I'M NANCY DREW, GIRL DETECTIVE. SO, I'M NOT ONE TO BE *MYSTIFIED* FOR LONG – NOT IF I CAN HELP IT.

I'VE INVESTIGATED LOTS OF "IMPOSSIBLE" THINGS. AND BEHIND MOST MAGIC THERE'S A PERFECTLY EXPLAINABLE...

...TRICK.

CHAPTER ONE:
ILLUSION CONFUSION

MY BEST FRIENDS BESS AND GEORGE ARE COUSINS. THE THREE OF US ARE PRETTY DIFFERENT, BUT WE ALL DEFINITELY SEE THINGS FOR WHAT THEY ARE...

WE'RE RARELY DUPED BY APPEARANCES. ESPECIALLY GEORGE, WHO IS *ALWAYS SENSIBLE*.

OH, MY GOD! IT'S DAN DEVILLE! HE'S *FLOATING*!

NOW SHOWING

UH, WELL GEORGE HAD ALWAYS *APPEARED* SENSIBLE— UNTIL THE MAGIC HAPPENED.

AEE!////!!

GEORGE? ARE YOU ALL RIGHT?

DON'T TELL ME *YOU'RE* A... A *FAN*?!

⇶PANT⇷ OKAY! AFTER MY PARENTS TOLD ME THE EASTER BUNNY WASN'T REAL, I WAS DEVASTATED. I WANTED TO BELIEVE IN MAGIC SO BAD.

SO, THEY TOOK ME TO SEE DAN DEVILLE — HE WAS THE MOST AMAZING MAGICIAN I'VE EVER SEEN!

ALTHOUGH, THE SHOW WAS MORE FUN NOW THAT I KNEW THE CHARACTERS BETTER.

FOR MY LAST TRICK, LOVELY TINA WILL ASSIST ME BY STEPPING INTO WHAT I CALL THE *GIRL BOX*! I WILL NEED AN INSPECTOR FROM THE AUDIENCE.

WHO WILL CONFIRM THERE IS NO WAY OUT OF THE BOX EXCEPT THE SAME WAY TINA STEPPED IN?!

THE LOVELY YOUNG LADY IN THE FIRST ROW, *PLEASE!*

HE MEANT *ME*. I'M NOT SURE WHY I RAISED MY HAND. I JUST HEARD THE WORD *INSPECTOR* AND WENT GAGA.

I GAVE THE BOX A THOROUGH GOING-OVER.

I SUSPECTED THERE WAS A TRAP DOOR. BUT, I DIDN'T NEED MY KEEN DETECTIVE SKILLS TO NOTICE THAT GEORGE WOULD KILL ME IF I *RUINED* IT FOR EVERYONE.

SO, I PLAYED ALONG.

APPEARS SOLID ENOUGH!

THANK YOU, SO MUCH! NOW, PLEASE STEP AWAY FROM THE BOX. NO TELLING HOW THE MAGIC WILL MANIFEST...

THE ENERGY HAS BEEN KNOWN TO TEMPORARILY *BLIND* THOSE TOO CLOSE.

THAT'S *CONVENIENT*.

ARUPABHAVA!!

I EXPECTED TINA TO BE GONE AFTER A KIND OF CHEAP, DISTRACTING LIGHT SHOW...

I HAD TO ADMIT IT WAS A *GOOD* TRICK! AND I COULDN'T HELP WONDERING HOW HE DID IT IN *PLAIN SIGHT* LIKE THAT.

WHEN DAN HAD SNAPPED HIS FINGERS, I BLINKED, AND WHILE MOST BLINKING IS INVOLUNTARILY – THIS HAD BEEN DIFFERENT.

MAYBE IT WAS A BLINK CAUSED BY A FLASH OF LIGHT – A VERY FAST *STROBE* YOU DON'T SEE AS MUCH AS *SENSE*

I DIDN'T SIT DOWN RIGHT AWAY, BECAUSE I FIGURED I'D WAIT 'TIL THE *END* OF THE TRICK.

BUT, APPARENTLY THAT'S ALL THERE WAS.

OUR LOVELY *INSPECTOR,* LADIES AND GENTLEMEN!

HE TRICK WAS OVER AND SO WAS THE SHOW.

THANKS FOLKS! I'M HERE EVERY WEEKEND THIS MONTH. GOOD NIGHT!

OKAY, EVEN YOU HAVE TO ADMIT THAT WAS PRETTY *AMAZING,* NANCY!

I ADMIT I'M NOT SURE *HOW* SHE DISAPPEARED. BUT, WHAT BUGS ME MORE IS THAT DAN ONLY DID *HALF* THE TRICK.

I WAS BORED BY SOME OF THE TRICKS, BUT, THIS ONE'S GOT ME SCRATCHING MY HEAD... AND YOU KNOW WHAT HAPPENS WHEN I SCRATCH MY HEAD?

THE ITCH GOES AWAY?

NO! THAT ITCH WON'T QUIT UNTIL WE *ALL* SOLVE THE MYSTERY!

A DISAPPEARING ACT ALMOST ALWAYS ENDS WITH THE MAGICIAN BRINGING *BACK* WHATEVER DISAPPEARED...

IT'S CALLED THE *PRESTIGE*, AND THE COOLEST WAY TO DO IT IS TO BRING IT BACK SOMEWHERE *ELSE*.

THAT'S WHY DAN KEPT LOOKING INTO THE BACK OF THE THEATER...HE WAS LOOKING FOR *TINA!*

CHAPTER TWO:
NOW YOU SEE HER,
NOW YOU DON'T!

SECURITY, THERE ARE THREE PEOPLE DOWN UNDER THE STAGE TRYING TO STEAL MY SECRETS... COME IMMEDIATELY AND REMOVE THEM.

≳SIGH≲ IF IT'S *SECRECY* YOU WANT, CALLING SECURITY WAS A BIG MISTAKE!

AFTER A SHOW, SECURITY GENERALLY GUARDS THE *STAGE DOOR...* THAT IS WHERE THE *REPORTERS* WAIT. SO IF THOSE GUARDS ARE SUDDENLY CALLED TO A CRIME SCENE...

IT DOESN'T TAKE A CRYSTAL BALL TO REALIZE THE *PRESS* WOULD BE SURE TO TRY AND GET THE *SCOOP.*

WHO'S STEALING YOUR *SECRETS,* MR. DEVILLE? DOES THIS *RUIN* YOUR ACT?

ANYONE...

...BEFORE MY SHOW ONE WEEK FROM TONIGHT, WHEN I WILL TRIUMPHANTLY MAKE HER *REAPPEAR!*

I HAD TO HAND IT TO HIM. DAN HAD PULLED A *PUBLICITY RABBIT* OUT OF HIS, UH, HAT...

UNTIL THEN, ADIEU!

THEN HE DISAPPEARED... SORT OF.

SO THEN IT WAS ALL PART OF THE *ACT*, RIGHT, NANCY? A GREAT *TRICK* AND A GREAT *PUBLICITY* STUNT?

NANCY? WAS IT A PLANNED PART THE ACT, OR NOT?

WELL...

NO TRESPA
VIOLATORS WILL B

I'M NOT SO SURE...

THUD

BANG

SLAM

IN A WAY, IT DIDN'T MATTER! EITHER WAY, IT WAS A *MYSTERY*! ONE WE'D ALL BEEN *INVITED* TO SOLVE!

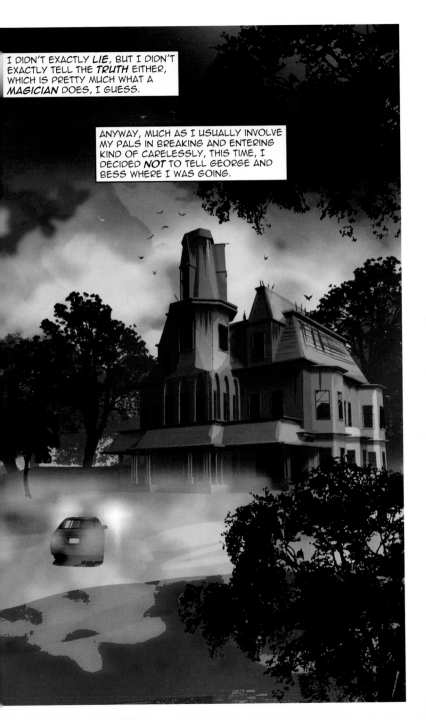

I DIDN'T EXACTLY *LIE*, BUT I DIDN'T EXACTLY TELL THE *TRUTH* EITHER, WHICH IS PRETTY MUCH WHAT A *MAGICIAN* DOES, I GUESS.

ANYWAY, MUCH AS I USUALLY INVOLVE MY PALS IN BREAKING AND ENTERING KIND OF CARELESSLY, THIS TIME, I DECIDED *NOT* TO TELL GEORGE AND BESS WHERE I WAS GOING.

GEORGE STILL WANTED TO BELIEVE IN DAN'S MAGIC. THE HOUSE WOULD BE *FULL* OF EVIDENCE TO THE CONTRARY. I DIDN'T WANT TO BE THE ONE TO PROVE THERE WAS NO TOOTH FAIRY UNLESS I *HAD* TO.

OF COURSE, I COULD JUST KNOCK, BUT EVEN IF DAN *DID* WELCOME ME IN TO LOOK AROUND...

...ANY EVIDENCE OF WHAT HAPPENED TO TINA WOULDN'T BE LEFT LYING AROUND WHERE I COULD *EASILY* FIND IT.

HE WAS A PROFESSIONAL *MAGICIAN*, AFTER ALL. WHICH IS WHY I WAITED DOWN THE BLOCK FOR HOURS UNTIL HE WENT OUT.

EVEN WITH THE MOON SO BRIGHT, IT WAS PRETTY DARK IN THE OLD BENSEN HOUSE. IT'D BEEN EMPTY SINCE THE OWNER PASSED AWAY IN 2002.

I STILL COULDN'T TURN ON ANY LIGHTS, IN CASE DAN CAME BACK OR THE NEIGHBORS WERE WATCHING.

I HAD MY TRUSTY FLASHLIGHT, THOUGH, SO IT WAS EASY TO SPOT THE...

...TIGER!

≳GASP!≲

I WAS RIGHT NOT TO BRING GEORGE.

SHE'D HAVE BEEN DEPRESSED TO SEE THE LEVITATION WIRES AND MACHINE UP CLOSE.

A MANUFACTURER IN VEGAS MAKES THE WIRES LESS THAN A MILLIMETER WIDE, ALMOST INVISIBLE, BUT EACH ONE CAN HOLD UP TO 100 KILOGRAMS.

A COOL THING, BUT FOR SOME, NOT AS COOL AS *MAGIC*.

THAT'S WHY SO MANY PEOPLE BELIEVE THAT DAN CAN MAKE AN ELEPHANT DISAPPEAR BEFORE THEIR VERY EYES.

NEVER MIND THAT HE USED A *CURTAIN* AND, WELL...

...AS ONE MAGICIAN ONCE SAID, IT'S NOT MAGIC, IT'S A *TRICK*!

NOTHING.

NOT SURE WHAT I WAS EXPECTING, MAYBE JUST A CLUE OR TWO ABOUT WHY AND HOW TINA MIGHT HAVE VANISHED.

EVEN THOUGH DAN LOOKED MORE SURPRISED THAN I WAS ABOUT HER DISAPPEARANCE, IT *COULD* HAVE BEEN AN ACT. HE MAKES A PRETTY GOOD LIVING FOOLING PEOPLE.

⋛SNIFF. SNIFF.⋚ JUDGING BY THE BIG CAGE AND THE ANIMAL SMELL, I WASN'T *ALONE* IN HERE.

OR WAS I?

CONSIDERING THE SIZE OF THE EMPTY CAGE, THAT WAS *ANOTHER* QUESTION I WASN'T SURE I WANTED TO KNOW THE ANSWER TO.

AND HERE I THOUGHT *DETECTIVES* WERE ALWAYS *DYING* FOR ANSWERS.

UH, DID I MENTION I SOMETIMES BECOME SO *SINGLE-MINDED* ABOUT LOOKING FOR CLUES, I FORGET THINGS, LIKE CHECKING TO SEE IF MY HYBRID CAR'S BATTERY IS CHARGED, AND...

CLICK

CLICK

...IF A DOOR IS *LOCKED* FROM THE INSIDE.

I REALLY, REALLY *HOPED* IT WAS JUST ONE OF THE OLD HOUSE'S NOISY STEAM HEAT RADIATORS.

HSSSSSS

BUT THERE WAS THAT *POSTER* WITH THE... YOU KNOW...

OH, DARN.

GREEN ANACONDAS ARE THE LARGEST SNAKES IN THE WORLD. THE FEMALES CAN GROW TO MORE THAN 29 FEET AND WEIGH MORE THAN 550 POUNDS.

I HAD A FUNNY FEELING *THIS* WAS FEMALE.

AND WHILE ANACONDAS ARE PARTICULARLY DEADLY IN *WATER*, KNOWING THAT DIDN'T MAKE ME FEEL ANY BETTER.

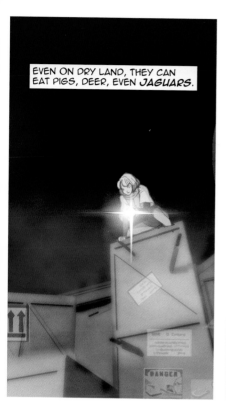

EVEN ON DRY LAND, THEY CAN EAT PIGS, DEER, EVEN *JAGUARS*.

COILING AROUND CAPTURED PREY, THEY SQUEEZE UNTIL THE ANIMAL *ASPHYXIATES*.

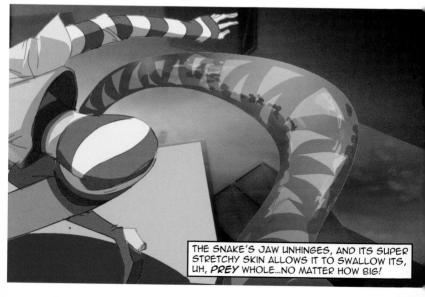

THE SNAKE'S JAW UNHINGES, AND ITS SUPER STRETCHY SKIN ALLOWS IT TO SWALLOW ITS, UH, *PREY* WHOLE...NO MATTER HOW BIG!

GOING BY HOW AGGRESSIVE SHE WAS BEING, I SUSPECTED DAN MIGHT HAVE GONE OUT TO GET *DINNER* FOR HER.

HssSSSSSSSS!

THERE ARE SOME PHOTOS SUPPOSEDLY SHOWING THE RESULTS (YECHHH!), BUT THESE WERE SHOWN TO BE *FAKE!*

OF COURSE, NO ONE'S EVER *PROVEN* THAT AN ANACONDA'S EVER SWALLOWED A *PERSON*, SUCH AS, SAY, A *GIRL DETECTIVE*, WHOLE.

WHETHER IT ACTUALLY *SWALLOWED* ME OR NOT, IT COULD STILL *KILL* ME JUST BY WRAPPING ITS *TAIL* AROUND SOMETHING FOR LEVERAGE AND *PULLING*.

PAST ITS STRETCHY SKIN, GREEN ANACONDAS ARE ALL *MUSCLE*. IN THE JUNGLE, FINDING A STRONG BRANCH WOULD BE *EASY*.

HERE, NOT SO MUCH. I COULD SEE ITS TAIL TWITCHING, SEARCHING.

WHICH GAVE ME AN IDEA.

FOR A SECOND THERE, I WAS AFRAID IT DIDN'T REALLY CARE IT WAS TOUCHING A *HOT* RADIATOR.

HsssSSSSSS!

HsssSSSSSS!

BUT IT DID.

SHAHHAHACKKSSSS!

NOW, I'D NEVER HURT *ANYONE*, LET ALONE A GIANT REPTILE, IF I DIDN'T HAVE TO...

...BUT IT *WAS* TRYING TO EAT ME.

NO! I DON'T NEED SOME STARSTRUCK SECRETARY! I NEED *ANSWERS*.

SECRETARY?

OH, HE SHOULDN'T HAVE SAID *THAT*.

TO AVOID A BLOW-UP, I STARTED TALKING FAST.

I'M NOT *SURE* THIS IS A KIDNAPPING, BUT MISSING PERSON CASES SHOULD ALWAYS BE SOLVED *QUICKLY*, SO IF I COULD MAKE A SUGGES-TION...

RIGHT... TIME IS OF THE ESSENCE. SO ENOUGH OF THIS CHIT-CHAT. LET'S GET TO WORK. HERE.

WHAT'S THIS?

IT'S A LIST OF MY ENEMIES, OTHER MAGICIANS AND RIVALS WHO'D LIKE TO SEE ME TOPPLED.

MAGICAL ENEMIES? LIKE VOLDEMORT?

LOOK, MR. DEVILLE, WHEN I SAID WE SHOULD WORK *TOGETHER*, THIS IS *NOT* WHAT I HAD IN MIND...

I HAVE MY OWN WAY OF DOING THINGS AND I'VE BEEN PRETTY...

THEN, HERE'S YOUR CHANCE TO LEARN A *BETTER* WAY!

SLAM

THAT NIGHT, I KNEW DAN WAS REALLY *SUFFERING*, SO I DIDN'T ARGUE ABOUT WEARING THE SHINY COSTUME!

LADIES AND GENTLEMEN, I KNOW I PROMISED TO BRING BACK MY ASSISTANT WHO DISAPPEARED FROM THIS STAGE DURING MY LAST PER-FORMANCE...

BUT, TONIGHT, I AM VERY SORRY TO ANNOUNCE TO ALL OF YOU THAT TINA SEEMS TO BE LOST, *FOREVER!*

THE AUDIENCE DIDN'T TAKE THE NEWS WELL AT ALL.

bOO! hiSSs! liar!

IT WAS CLEAR DAN HAD NEVER BEEN *BOOED* BEFORE.

HE WAS LIKE A DEER CAUGHT IN THE HEADLIGHTS.

IT WAS NATURAL FOR BESS AND GEORGE TO WORRY.

YOU CAN *STOP* WAVING NOW!

OH! SORRY.

AFTER ALL, THEY'D *SEEN* DAN SCREW UP THIS TRICK, BEFORE.

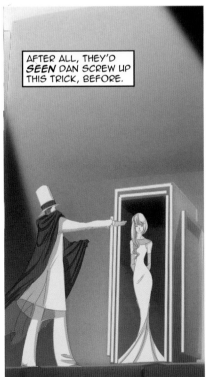

HE MANAGED TO LOSE *ONE* LOVELY ASSISTANT... WHAT WAS TO STOP HIM FROM LOSING ANOTHER?

THE DISAPPEARING DETECTIVE TRICK
HAS TO HAPPEN VERY *FAST*...

YOU CAN'T GIVE THE AUDIENCE
TIME TO THINK ABOUT IT.

I COULD HEAR DAN'S PYROTECHNICS AND KNEW
THAT THE AUDIENCE WAS SEEING SMOKE AND A
FLASH DESIGNED TO DAZZLE AND DISTRACT...

...JUST LONG ENOUGH FOR
THE *MAGIC* TO HAPPEN.

WHILE THE CROWD CHEERED AGAIN... THIS TIME TO SEE THE GIRL DETECTIVE MAGICALLY **REAPPEAR** IN THE BACK OF THE THEATER, I GAVE THE GIRLS A BREAK AND EXPLAINED.

SEE, I REMEMBERED TINA HAD GIVEN DAN AN **ULTIMATUM**... HE HAD TO LET HER DO A SOLO ACT **AND** HE HAD TO SHOW UP FOR THEIR **ANNIVERSARY** DATE.

AFTER SOME SNOOPING, I DISCOVERED THE ANNIVERSARY WAS **TODAY**.

SO, I HUNTED IN ALL THE NICEST "BIG DATE" PLACES IN TOWN UNTIL I FOUND TINA... **ALONE**.

SHE HAD LEFT DAN, JUST TO **PROVE** THAT SHE COULD. SHE STILL LOVED HIM, BUT WAS FED UP WITH HIS **ARROGANCE**.

AND WHO KNOWS?

THAT KIND OF LOVE COULD HAVE THE POWER TO CHANGE EVEN THE MOST *OBSESSED* MIND!

LADIES AND GENTLE-MEN!

TONIGHT, I HAVE THE PRIVILEGE OF PRESENTING MY LOVELY AND TALENTED *PARTNER*, TINA WHO WILL NOW PERFORM HER VERY FIRST, VERY *OWN* FEAT OF MAGIC!

AND PRESTO! LOOKS LIKE IT EVEN WORKED ON DAN.

LITTLE DID I REALIZE IT BUT DAN WASN'T THE ONLY ONE TO GET PLEASANTLY TRICKED THAT NIGHT!

NED AND TINA CONSPIRED AFTER THE SHOW TO GET A RESERVATION AT THAT SAME FANCY RESTAURANT.

NOBODY NEEDED TO TWIST DAN'S OR MY ARM TO GO, THOUGH. WE'D **SORT OF** LEARNED OUR LESSONS

YES, I ADMIT I NEED TO SPEND MORE TIME **WORKING**...

...ON MY **RELATION-SHIP** WITH YOU, OF COURSE!

OKAY. SO, DAN'S *ATTITUDE* NEEDED SOME ADJUSTING.

HEY, NED PROBABLY FELT MINE DID, TOO.

BUT, SOMETIMES WHAT WE LOVE ABOUT A PERSON ISN'T THEIR ATTITUDE...

IT'S THEIR *STYLE*...

...THEIR *TECHNIQUE*...

...THAT MAKES THEM TRULY SPECIAL.

THE END

The Tenacious Teen Sleuth Faces Her Biggest Mystery Yet!

During her initiation case to gain entry into the prestigious Clue Bender Society, Nancy is swept up in an alarming theft that snowballs into a dramatic whodunit. With only 24 hours to secure her membership and unravel the mystery, Nancy will have to be at the top of her game!

Use Nancy's new fingerprint identifier and the DS Microphone to discover hidden clues

New snowmobile and boat play lets Nancy thoroughly explore the Clue Bender's Island

Play through 9 intriguing chapters filled with sleuthing and secrecy

Available Now!
majescoentertainment.com

NINTENDO DS

MAJESCO
ENTERTAINMENT

...THEY DON'T ALWAYS *BEHAVE* LIKE PETS!

HHH!

HSSSS

IT'S ALL RIGHT, NANCY. EVEN *I* STILL GET A LITTLE JITTERY AROUND THE CRITTERS WITH THAT MANY TEETH.

JACK MARVIN RAN THE RIVER HEIGHTS ANIMAL PROTECTION CENTER. HE'D SAVED JUST ABOUT EVERY IMAGINABLE KIND OF ABANDONED, LOST OR MISTREATED PET.

I'M USUALLY BUSY SOLVING MYSTERIES WITH MY BEST FRIENDS, GEORGE AND BESS.

BUT, MYSTERIES HAD BEEN IN SHORT SUPPLY, LATELY, SO WE ALL DECIDED TO GET IN TOUCH WITH OUR INNER ANIMAL LOVERS BY *VOLUNTEERING*.

WE DROVE DEEP INTO THE RIVER HEIGHTS WOODS TO THE COTTAGE OF MRS. EARTHA.

GIVEN HER LOCATION, IT WAS NO BIG SURPRISE SHE WAS HAVING CLOSE ENCOUNTERS WITH WILDLIFE.

BIG MONGREL CARRIED MY POOR *TUNSIS* INTO THE SHED! GET HIM!

IT'S A DOG EAT CAT WORLD AND SOMETIMES NATURE SEEMS CRUEL.

BUT, WHILE *HUMANS* ARE THE *DEADLIEST* CREATURE ON THE PLANET...

DON'T MISS NANCY DREW #15 – "TIGER COUNTER"

THE HARDY BOYS®

A NEW GRAPHIC NOVEL EVERY 3 MONTHS!

#1 "The Ocean of Osyria"
ISBN 1-59707-001-7

#2 "Identity Theft" ISBN 1-59707-003-3

#3 "Mad House" ISBN 1-59707-010-6

#4 "Malled" ISBN 1-59707-014-9

#5 "Sea You, Sea Me!" ISBN 1-59707-022-X

#6 "Hyde & Shriek" ISBN 1-59707-028-9

#7 "The Opposite Numbers..."
ISBN 1-59707-034-8

#8 "Board to Death" ISBN 1-59707-053-X

#9 "To Die, Or Not To Die?"
ISBN 1-59707-062-9

#10 "A Hardy Day's Night"
ISBN 1-59707-070-X

#11 "Abracadeath"
ISBN 1-59707-080-7

NEW! #12 "Dude Ranch O' Death!"
ISBN 1-59707-088-2

ON SALE NOW!

All: Pocket sized, 96-112pp., full color, $7.95
Also available in hardcover! $12.95 each.

NEW STORY! FULL-COLOR GRAPHIC NOV

THE HARDY BOYS

#12 DUDE RANCH O'DEATH

based on the series by Franklin W. Dixon

Scott LOBDELL
Paulo HENRIQUE

UNDERCOVER BROTHERS™

PAPERCUTZ

The Hardy Boys ®Simon & Schuster

Hardy Boys Boxed Set #1-4

384 pages of color comics!
$29.95
ISBN 1-59707-040-8

Hardy Boys Boxed Set #5-8

432 pages of color comics!
$29.95
ISBN 1-59707-075-0

ZORRO

#1 "Scars!"   ISBN 1-59707-016-5

#2 "Drownings!"   ISBN 1-59707-018-1

#3 "Vultures!" ISBN 1-59707-020-3

Each: 5x7½, 96pp., full color paperback: $7.95
Also available in hardcover! $12.95 each.

ALL-NEW, FULL-COLOR GRAPHIC NOVE

ZORRO

#1 SCARS!

DON McGREGOR • SIDNEY LIMA

SEE THE NEW MAJOR MOTION PICTURE "THE LEGEND OF ZORRO"

PAPERCUTZ

© 2008 Zorro Productions, Inc. All rights reserved.

At your store or order at Papercutz, 40 Exchange Place, Ste. 1308,
New York NY 10005, 1-800-886-1223

PAPERCUTZ

CAMPUS

WITHDRAWN